Improving
Writing

for ages 7–8

A & C Black • London

Contents

Andrew Brodie: Improving Writing for ages 7–8 © A&C Black Publishers 2010

Improving Writing presents a variety of stimulating activities to help pupils make progress with a wide range of writing skills.

So, what do we mean by 'improving writing'? Do we mean improving technical skills such as spelling, handwriting and punctuation? Or do we mean improving creative skills such as story-writing, descriptive work and poetry? The answer of course, is that we are seeking to improve a range of both technical and creative skills. This range is specified in the national guidelines for the assessment of writing, a summary of which is provided on page 5-7.

How to use this book

Each unit consists of four pages. The first page, 'Text for Talking', is a model text that features the main text and a suggested learning objective. Then follows three worksheets at different levels to enable teachers to differentiate across the ability range. An animal picture at the top of the sheet indicates the level of the worksheet. The 'cat' exercises are at the simplest level; the 'dog' exercises are at the next level; the 'rabbit' exercises are at the most advanced level: Cat worksheets are for pupils working at Level 1, progressing towards Level 2; Dog worksheets are for pupils working at Level 2; Rabbit worksheets are for pupils who are working confidently at Level 2 and are achieving aspects of Level 3. There is a class record sheet on page 64 to record progress.

How to use the CD-ROM

The accompanying CD-ROM contains printable and photocopiable PDFs of all the worksheets. All the photographs featured on the worksheets are also provided to enable you to display them in full colour on the whiteboard.

The guidelines for assessing writing

The guidelines for assessing writing at Level 1 suggest what the pupils should achieve 'in some writing, usually with support', those for assessing writing at Level 2 indicate what pupils should achieve 'in some forms of writing' and those for assessing writing at Level 3 suggest what pupils should achieve 'in most writing'. Note that each Assessment Focus has a sub-title that shows what pupils are working towards. In Assessment Focus 4, for example, the pupils are working towards 'constructing paragraphs and using cohesion within and between paragraphs' but the bullet points indicate that pupils at Level 1, Level 2 or Level 3 are at the early stages of this process: we would not expect Year 3 pupils to write a text consisting of a set of well-structured paragraphs!

Assessing writing record sheet

You may wish to use this sheet on several occasions to record a 'snapshot' of your current class. Which children would you classify as working at Level 1, which at Level 2 and which at Level 3? The guidelines for assessing each level are shown on pages 5–7.

Level 1
Pupils' writing communicates meaning through simple words and phrases. In their reading or their writing, pupils begin to show awareness of how full stops are used. Letters are usually clearly shaped and correctly orientated.

Level 2
Pupils' writing communicates meaning in both narrative and non-narrative forms, using appropriate and interesting vocabulary, and showing some awareness of the reader. Ideas are developed in a sequence of sentences, sometimes demarcated by capital letters and full stops. Simple, monosyllabic words are usually spelt correctly, and where there are inaccuracies the alternative is phonetically plausible. In handwriting, letters are accurately formed and consistent in size.

Level 3
Pupils' writing is often organised, imaginative and clear. The main features of different forms of writing are used appropriately, beginning to be adapted to different readers. Sequences of sentences extend ideas logically and words are chosen for variety and interest. The basic grammatical structure of sentences is usually correct. Spelling is usually accurate, including that of common, polysyllabic words. Punctuation to mark sentences – full stops, capital letters and question marks – is used accurately. Handwriting is joined and legible.

Andrew Brodie: Improving Writing for ages 7–8 © A&C Black Publishers 2010

Guidelines for assessing writing at Level 1

You may wish to use this sheet as an individual record sheet by ticking the statements when you feel that pupils are secure in the specific skills that these represent. The National Curriculum Attainment Target for Writing Levels 1, 2 and 3 are shown on page 4.

Handwriting and presentation:
☐ Most letters are correctly formed and orientated.
☐ There are spaces between words.
☐ Upper and lower case letters are sometimes distinguished.
☐ ICT is used, eg for typing own name.

Assessment Focus 1 – write imaginative, interesting and thoughtful texts:
☐ Basic information and ideas are conveyed through appropriate word choice, eg related to a topic.
☐ Some descriptive language is used, eg colour, size, simple emotion.

Assessment Focus 2 – produce texts, which are appropriate to task, reader and purpose:
☐ There is some indication of basic purpose, particular form or awareness of reader, eg story, label, message.

Assessment Focus 3 – organise and present whole texts effectively, sequencing and structuring information, ideas and events:
☐ Some formulaic phrases indicate start/end of text, eg once upon a time, one day, the end.
☐ Events and ideas are sometimes in appropriate order, eg actions listed in time sequence, items numbered.

Assessment Focus 4 – construct paragraphs and use cohesion within and between paragraphs:
☐ Simple connections between ideas and events, eg repeated nouns, pronouns relate to main idea.

Assessment Focus 5 – vary sentences for clarity, purpose and effect:
☐ Reliance on simple phrases and clauses.
☐ Some sentence-like structures formed by chaining clauses together, eg series of ideas joined by repeated use of 'and'.

Assessment Focus 6 – write with technical accuracy of syntax and punctuation in phrases, clauses and sentences:
☐ Mostly grammatically accurate clauses.
☐ Some awareness of use of full stops and capital letters, eg beginning, end of sentence.

Assessment Focus 7 – select appropriate and effective vocabulary:
☐ Mostly simple vocabulary.
☐ Communicates meaning through repetition of key words.

Assessment Focus 8 – use correct spelling:
☐ Usually correct spelling of simple high frequency words.
☐ Phonetically plausible attempts at words with digraphs and double letters.
☐ Sufficient number of recognisable words for writing to be readable, including, eg use of letter names to approximate symbols and words.

Guidelines for assessing writing at Level 2

You may wish to use this sheet as an individual record sheet by ticking the statements when you feel that pupils are secure in the specific skills that these represent. The National Curriculum Attainment Target for Writing Levels 1, 2 and 3 are shown on page 4.

Handwriting and presentation:
☐ Letters are generally correctly shaped but there may be some inconsistencies in orientation, size and use of upper or lower case letters.
☐ Letters are clearly formed, with ascenders and descenders distinguished.
☐ Upper and lower case letters are not generally mixed within words.

Assessment Focus 1 – write imaginative, interesting and thoughtful texts:
☐ In some forms of writing there are mostly relevant ideas and content, though sometimes it is repetitive or sparse.
☐ Some apt word choices create interest.
☐ Brief comments, questions about events or actions suggest viewpoint.

Assessment Focus 2 – produce texts, which are appropriate to task, reader and purpose:
☐ There is some basic purpose established, eg main features of story, report.
☐ Some appropriate features of the given form are used.
☐ There are some attempts to adopt appropriate style.

Assessment Focus 3 – organise and present whole texts effectively, sequencing and structuring information, ideas and events:
☐ There is some basic sequencing of ideas or material, eg time-related words or phrases, line breaks, headings, numbers.
☐ Openings and/or closings are sometimes signalled.

Assessment Focus 4 – construct paragraphs and use cohesion within and between paragraphs:
☐ In some forms of writing ideas are in sections, grouped by content, some linking by simple pronouns.

Assessment Focus 5 – vary sentences for clarity, purpose and effect:
☐ Some variation in sentence openings, eg not always starting with a name or pronoun.
☐ There are mainly simple sentences with 'and' used to connect clauses.
☐ The past and present tenses are generally consistent.

Assessment Focus 6 – write with technical accuracy of syntax and punctuation in phrases, clauses and sentences:
☐ Clause structure mostly grammatically correct.
☐ Sentence demarcation with capital letters and full stops is usually accurate.
☐ There is some accurate use of question marks, exclamation marks and commas in lists.

Assessment Focus 7 – select appropriate and effective vocabulary:
☐ Simple, often speech-like vocabulary conveys relevant meanings.
☐ There are some adventurous word choices, eg opportune use of new vocabulary.

Assessment Focus 8 – use correct spelling:
☐ Usually correct spelling of high frequency grammatical function words and common single-morpheme content/lexical words. There are likely to be errors in inflected word endings, eg past tense, plurals and adverbs, and in phonetic attempts at vowel digraphs.

Guidelines for assessing writing at Level 3

You may wish to use this sheet as an individual record sheet by ticking the statements when you feel that pupils are secure in the specific skills that these represent. The National Curriculum Attainment Target for Writing Levels 1, 2 and 3 are shown on page 4.

Handwriting and presentation:
- [ ] A legible style
- [ ] Accurate and consistent letter formation
- [ ] Sometimes joined writing

Assessment Focus 1 – write imaginative, interesting and thoughtful texts:
- [ ] Some appropriate ideas and content are included.
- [ ] There is some attempt to elaborate on basic information or events, eg nouns are expanded by simple adjectives.
- [ ] There is an attempt to adopt viewpoint, though often not maintained or inconsistent, eg attitude expressed, but with little elaboration.

Assessment Focus 2 – produce texts, which are appropriate to task, reader and purpose:
- [ ] Purpose is established at a general level.
- [ ] Main features of a selected form are sometimes signalled to the reader.
- [ ] There are some attempts at appropriate style, with attention to the reader.

Assessment Focus 3 – organise and present whole texts effectively, sequencing and structuring information, ideas and events:
- [ ] There is some attempt to organise ideas with related points placed next to each other.
- [ ] Openings and closings are usually signalled.
- [ ] There is some attempt to sequence ideas or material logically.

Assessment Focus 4 – construct paragraphs and use cohesion within and between paragraphs:
- [ ] There is some internal structure within sections of text, eg one-sentence paragraphs or ideas loosely organised.
- [ ] Within paragraphs or sections there are some links between sentences, eg use of pronouns or adverbials.
- [ ] The movement between paragraphs/sections is sometimes abrupt or disjointed.

Assessment Focus 5 – vary sentences for clarity, purpose and effect:
- [ ] There is reliance mainly on simply structured sentences.
- [ ] There is some variation with support, eg some complex sentences.
- [ ] The most common connectives are and, but and so.
- [ ] There is some limited variation in use of tense and verb form, though not always secure.

Assessment Focus 6 – write with technical accuracy of syntax and punctuation in phrases, clauses and sentences:
- [ ] Straightforward sentences are usually demarcated accurately with full stops, capital letters, question marks and exclamation marks.
- [ ] There is some limited use of speech punctuation.
- [ ] Comma splicing is evident, particularly in narrative.

Assessment Focus 7 – select appropriate and effective vocabulary:
- [ ] Simple, generally appropriate vocabulary is used, although limited in range.
- [ ] Some words are selected for effect or occasion.

Assessment Focus 8 – use correct spelling:
- [ ] Correct spelling of some common grammatical function words.
- [ ] Correct spelling of common content/lexical words with more than one morpheme, including compound words.

(Likely to be errors with some inflected endings, eg past tense, comparatives, adverbs. Likely to be errors with some phonetically plausible attempts at content/lexical words.)

My summer holidays

Text for Talking

In the summer holidays I went to the seaside with my family. Every day we went to the beach. We set up an area of the beach as our base.

First of all we put up a windbreak. We had to bash the poles into the sand. Then we spread out our towels so that we could lie down to sunbathe.

I didn't sunbathe much! I went in the sea with my mum every day. One day I built a really big sandcastle.

I didn't want to come home at the end of the week.

Teacher's Notes

Suggested objective: Write descriptively about the summer holidays.
Read together: the text, consisting of a recount.
Talk together: Discuss the tatory with the children, encouraging them to think about their own holidays.
WOW (write own work): Choose the Cat worksheet, the Dog worksheet or the Rabbit worksheet, according to the ability level of each child. Support the child in following the instructions on the worksheet, to write their own work.

Andrew Brodie: Improving Writing for ages 7–8 © A&C Black Publishers 2010

My summary holidays

Name

Date

*Can you write about
the summer holidays?*

My summer holidays

In the summer holidays --

My summer holidays

Can you write about the summer holidays?

My summer holidays

In the summer holidays --

First of all --

After that ---

Finally --

Andrew Brodie: Improving Writing for ages 7–8 © A&C Black Publishers 2010

My summer holidays

Name
Date

Can you write about the summer holidays?

My summer holidays

Teacher's Notes

Read together: the text on page 8, 'My summer holidays', then the instructions on this page.
Talk together: Discuss the text with the children. Can they observe the structure of the report?
WOW (write own work): Encourage the children to write about their own summer holidays.
- Are some appropriate ideas included? Are simple adjectives used to elaborate on information or events? Is there an attempt to adopt viewpoint? (AF1 Level 3)
- Is purpose established at a general level? (AF2 Level 3)
- Is there some attempt to sequence ideas and material logically, eg with related points placed next to each other? (AF3 Level 3)
- Is there some structure within sections of text? Are there some links between sentences? (AF4 Level 3)
- Are sentences demarcated accurately with capital letters and full stops, question marks or exclamation marks? (AF6 Level 3)
- Is appropriate vocabulary used, and are some words chosen for effect? (AF7 Level 3)
- Does the child use correct spelling? (AF8 Level 3)

A drink for a crow

Text for Talking

One hot summer's day all the animals and birds were very thirsty. There had been no rain for days and the ponds and streams had all dried up. The creatures couldn't find a place to drink anywhere. Then a clever crow spotted a jug of water that a human had put out on a table.

The crow flew over to the table and tried to drink from the jug but however hard he tried, he couldn't reach the water. He flew down to the ground and picked up a stone in his beak. Then he flew back up and dropped the stone into the jug. He kept flying down to the ground and picking up stones to drop into the jug. Each time he dropped a stone into the jug, the level of the water went up.

At last there were enough stones in the water. The water had risen close to the top of the jug. The crow was able to reach the water to have a nice long drink.

Teacher's Notes

Suggested objective: Write a story in clear sections.
Read together: the text, consisting of a story based on an Aesop's fable.
Talk together: Discuss the story with the children. It would be very helpful to demonstrate the science involved in the story: use a clear jug or glass containing water, then add pebbles to the water to demonstrate the rise in water level.
WOW (write own work): Choose the Cat worksheet, the Dog worksheet or the Rabbit worksheet, according to the ability level of each child. Support the child in following the instructions on the worksheet, to write their own work.

 Andrew Brodie: Improving Writing for ages 7–8 © A&C Black Publishers 2010

A drink for a crow

Name

Date

*Can you finish the story
of the thirsty crow?*

A drink for a crow, from the fable by Aesop

One hot summer's day all the animals and birds were very thirsty. There had been no rain for days and the ponds and streams had all dried up. The creatures couldn't find a place to drink anywhere. Then a clever crow spotted a jug of water that a human had put out on a table.

The crow flew over to the table and tried to drink from the jug but however hard he tried, he couldn't reach the water. He flew down to the ground and picked up a stone in his beak. Then he flew back up and dropped the stone into the jug. He kept flying down to the ground and picking up stones to drop into the jug. Each time he dropped a stone into the jug, the level of the water went up.

Teacher's Notes

Read together: the text on page 12, 'A drink for a crow', then the instructions on this page and the words in the word bank. Read the first two paragraphs that are supplied.
Talk together: Discuss the text with the children. Can they understand the story? Discuss the first two paragraphs then encourage the children to tell the rest of the story orally.
WOW (write own work): Support the group in completing the story.
- Are basic information and ideas conveyed through appropriate word choice and is some descriptive writing used? (AF1 Level 1)
- Are there some simple connections between ideas and events? (AF4 Level 1)
- Are some sentence-like structures formed by chaining clauses together, eg by using 'and'? (AF5 Level 1)
- Is there some awareness of use of full stops and capital letters? (AF6 Level 1)
- Does the child select appropriate and effective vocabulary? (AF7 Level 1)
- Does the child use correct spelling? (AF8 Level 1)

A drink for a crow

Name

Date

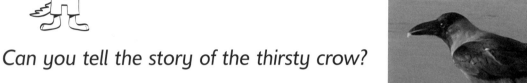

Can you tell the story of the thirsty crow?

A drink for a crow

One hot day --

The crow saw a jug --

He put --

At last ---

A drink for a crow

Can you tell the story of the thirsty crow?

A drink for a crow

Teacher's Notes

Read together: the text on page 12, 'A drink for a crow', then the instructions on this page.
Talk together: Discuss the text with the children. Can they understand the story?
WOW (write own work): Encourage the children to rewrite the story of the crow.

- Are some appropriate ideas included? Are simple adjectives used to elaborate on information or events?
  Is there an attempt to adopt viewpoint? (AF1 Level 3)
- Is purpose established at a general level? Are main features of a selected form signalled to the reader?
  Are there some attempts to adopt the appropriate style? (AF2 Level 3)
- Is there some attempt to sequence ideas and material logically, eg with related points placed next to each
  other? Are openings and closings sometimes signalled? (AF3 Level 3)
- Is there some structure within sections of text? Are there some links between sentences? (AF4 Level 3)
- Is there reliance mainly on simply structured sentences, but with some variation with support? (AF5 Level 3)
- Are sentences demarcated accurately with capital letters and full stops, question marks or exclamation marks?
  (AF6 Level 3)
- Is appropriate vocabulary used, and are some words chosen for effect? (AF7 Level 3)
- Does the child use correct spelling? (AF8 Level 3)

The fox and the crow

The fox and the crow, from the fable by Aesop

One day a crow spotted a great big piece of cheese and flew down to pick it up. He flew up into a tree with the cheese held tightly in his beak.

Just then a fox came passing by and saw the crow in the tree. The fox was quite hungry himself and decided he wanted to eat the cheese.

"Hello, Crow!" called the fox.

The crow looked down at the fox and held on tightly to the cheese.

"You look very handsome," said the fox. "You are so handsome, you are like the king of all the birds!"

The crow looked down at the fox and held on tightly to the cheese. He was pleased that the fox had said he was handsome, because he thought so too!

"As you are so handsome, I am sure you have a beautiful voice too," said the fox. "I would love to hear you sing," he added.

The crow was so pleased that the fox admired him. He opened his beak wide to show how beautifully he could caw. But, as soon as he opened his beak, the piece of cheese fell out and dropped all the way to the ground.

The fox quickly gobbled up the cheese. "Thank you," he called. "That was an easy way to get a good meal!"

Teacher's Notes

Suggested objective: Write a story in clear sections.
Read together: the text, consisting of a story based on an Aesop's fable.
Talk together: Discuss the tstory with the children.
WOW (write own work): Choose the Cat worksheet, the Dog worksheet or the Rabbit worksheet, according to the ability level of each child. Support the child in following the instructions on the worksheet, to write their own work.

The fox and the crow

Name

Date

Word Bank crow fox cheese tree big eat beak piece sing beautiful beautifully handsome said fell dropped gobbled

One day a crow _____

_____

_____

_____

The fox said _____

_____

_____

_____

The crow opened _____

_____

_____

_____

The fox _____

_____

_____

_____

Teacher's Notes

Read together: the text on page 16, 'The fox and the crow', then the instructions on this page and the words in the word bank. Read the sentence starts that are supplied.

Talk together: Discuss the text with the children. Can they understand the story? Discuss the sentence starts then encourage the children to complete each sentence orally so that the main points of the story are covered.

WOW (write own work): Support the group in completing the story.
- Are basic information and ideas conveyed through appropriate word choice and is some descriptive writing used? (AF1 Level 1)
- Is the text appropriate to task, reader and purpose? (AF2 Levels 1&2)
- Are events and ideas presented in appropriate order? (AF3 Level 1)
- Are there some simple connections between ideas and events? (AF4 Level 1)
- Are some sentence-like structures formed by chaining clauses together, eg by using 'and'? (AF5 Level 1)
- Is there some awareness of use of full stops and capital letters? (AF6 Level 1)
- Does the child select appropriate and effective vocabulary? (AF7 Level 1)
- Does the child use correct spelling? (AF8 Level 1))

The fox and the crow

Teacher's Notes

Read together: the text on page 16, 'The fox and the crow'.

Talk together: Discuss the text with the children. Can they understand the story?

WOW (write own work): Support the group in writing at least one sentence for each section of the story.

- Are there mostly relevant ideas and content and do some apt word choices create interest? (AF1 Level 2)
- Is the text appropriate to task, reader and purpose? Is some basic purpose established? Are some appropriate features of the given form used? Are there some attempts to adopt the appropriate style? (AF2 Level 2)
- Is there some basic sequencing of ideas or material? Are openings and closings sometimes signalled? (AF3 Level 2)
- Are ideas grouped by content with some linking by simple pronouns? (AF4 Level 2)
- Is there some variation in sentence openings? Are there mainly simple sentences with 'and' used to connect clauses? Are the past and present tenses generally consistent? (AF5 Level 2)
- Are sentences usually accurately demarcated with capital letters and full stops and is clause structure mostly grammatically correct? (AF6 Level 2)
- Does simple vocabulary convey relevant meaning? Are there some adventurous word choices? (AF7 Level 2)
- Does the child use correct spelling? (AF8 Level 2)

Andrew Brodie: Improving Writing for ages 7–8 © A&C Black Publishers 2010

The fox and the crow

Name

Date

Can you tell the story of the fox and the crow?

The fox and the crow

Teacher's Notes

Read together: the text on page 16, 'The fox and the crow'.

Talk together: Discuss the text with the children. Can they understand the story?

WOW (write own work) Encourage the children to rewrite the story of the fox and the crow.
- Are some appropriate ideas included? Are simple adjectives used to elaborate on information or events? Is there an attempt to adopt viewpoint? (AF1 Level 3)
- Is purpose established at a general level? Are main features of a selected form signalled to the reader? Are there some attempts to adopt the appropriate style? (AF2 Level 3)
- Is there some attempt to sequence ideas and material logically, eg with related points placed next to each other? Are openings and closings sometimes signalled? (AF3 Level 3)
- Is there some structure within sections of text? Are there some links between sentences? (AF4 Level 3)
- Is there reliance mainly on simply structured sentences, but with some variation with support? (AF5 Level 3)
- Are sentences demarcated accurately with capital letters and full stops, question marks or exclamation marks? Is there some use of speech punctuation? (AF6 Level 3)
- Is appropriate vocabulary used, and are some words chosen for effect? (AF7 Level 3)
- Does the child use correct spelling? (AF8 Level 3)

Autumn leaves

The leaves in the autumn
Turn red and brown,
Before the wind
Brings them tumbling down.

The leaves in the autumn
Fall on to the ground,
Then my feet step through
With a scrunching sound.

The leaves in the autumn
Are blown away.
New leaves will grow
On a fresh spring day.

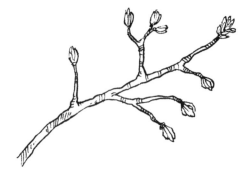

Teacher's Notes

Suggested objective: Write a poem following the style of 'Autumn Leaves'.
Read together: the rhyming poem.
Talk together: Discuss the poem with the children, pointing out that it rhymes and that it is written in a four-line structure. Encourage the children to observe the 'traditional' style of punctuation for rhyming poetry, ie capital letters at the start of each line.
WOW (write own work): Choose the Cat worksheet, the Dog worksheet or the Rabbit worksheet, according to the ability level of each child. Support the child in following the instructions on the worksheet, to write their own work.

Autumn leaves

Name

Date

Complete each verse of the poem.

Autumn leaves

The leaves in the autumn
Turn red and brown,

The leaves in the autumn
Fall on to the ground,

The leaves in the autumn
Are blown away.

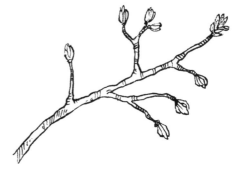

Teacher's Notes

This activity encourages children to observe the structure of a rhyming poem. It provides the opportunity for them to practise their skills in handwriting and in spelling using phonics, although many of the words they need are supplied in the word bank.

Read together: the poem on page 20, 'Autumn leaves', then the instructions on this page and the words in the word bank. Read the first two lines of each verse that are supplied.

Talk together: Discuss the poem with the children. If possible, take the children for a walk in leaves that have fallen in the autumn.

WOW (write own work): Dictate the second half of each verse, encouraging the children to write them neatly and to use appropriate spellings.

- Are most letters correctly formed and orientated? Are there appropriate spaces between words? Are upper and lower case letters distinguished? (Handwriting and presentation Level 1)
- Is there some awareness of use of full stops and capital letters? (AF6 Level 1)
- Does the child use correct spelling? (AF8 Level 1)

Autumn leaves

Name

Date

Complete each verse of the poem.

Autumn leaves

The leaves in the autumn
Turn red and brown,

The leaves in the autumn
Fall on to the ground,

The leaves in the autumn
Are blown away.

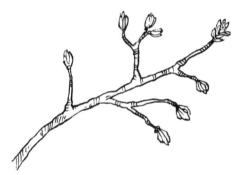

Teacher's Notes

This activity encourages children to observe the structure of a rhyming poem. It provides the opportunity for them to practise their skills in handwriting and in spelling using phonics.

Read together: the poem on page 20, 'Autumn leaves', then the instructions on this page. Read the first two lines of each verse that are supplied.

Talk together: Discuss the poem with the children. If possible, take the children for a walk in leaves that have fallen in the autumn.

WOW (write own work): Dictate the second half of each verse, encouraging the children to write them neatly and to use appropriate spellings.

● Are letters clearly formed, with ascenders and descenders distinguished? (Handwriting and presentation Level 2)
● Are sentences usually accurately demarcated with capital letters and full stops? (AF6 Level 2)
● Does the child use correct spelling? (AF8 Level 1)

Autumn leaves

Name

Date

Can you write two more verses for the poem?

Autumn leaves

The leaves in the autumn
Turn red and brown,
Before the wind
Brings them tumbling down.

The leaves in the autumn
Fall on to the ground,
Then my feet step through
With a scrunching sound.

The leaves in the autumn
Are blown away.
New leaves will grow
On a fresh spring day.

---------------------------------------   --

---------------------------------------   --

---------------------------------------   --

---------------------------------------   --

eacher's Notes

his activity encourages children to observe and follow the structure of a rhyming poem.

Read together: the question and the poem on this page.

Talk together: Discuss the poem with the children. If possible, take the children for a walk in leaves that have allen in the autumn and discuss the sights, sounds and smells.

WOW (write own work): Encourage the children to make up their own verses in a similar style to those in the poem.
- Are some appropriate ideas included? Are simple adjectives used to elaborate on information or events? Is there an attempt to adopt viewpoint? (AF1 Level 3)
- Is purpose established at a general level? Are main features of the rhyming poem form signalled to the reader? Are there some attempts to adopt the appropriate style? (AF2 Level 3)
- Is there some attempt to sequence ideas and material logically, eg with related points placed next to each other? Are openings and closings sometimes signalled? (AF3 Level 3)
- Is there some structure within sections of text? Are there some links between sentences? (AF4 Level 3)
- Is there reliance mainly on simply structured sentences, but with some variation with support? (AF5 Level 3)
- Are sentences demarcated accurately with capital letters and full stops, question marks or exclamation marks? (AF6 Level 3)
- Is appropriate vocabulary used, and are some words chosen for effect? (AF7 Level 3)
- Does the child use correct spelling? (AF8 Level 3)

My little dog

My little dog
Is a very strange dog,
He hops around,
Just like a frog!

The noise he makes
Is such a joke,
He doesn't bark,
He makes a croak!

My little dog
Is completely mad,
He tries to sit
On a lily pad!

When it tips
He tries to swim!
I have to say,
I do love him!

Teacher's Notes

Suggested objective: Write a poem following the style of 'My Little Dog'.
Read together: the rhyming poem.
Talk together: Discuss the poem with the children, pointing out that it rhymes and that it is written in a four-line structure. Encourage the children to observe the 'traditional' style of punctuation for rhyming poetry, eg capital letters at the start of each line. Explain that the exclamation marks are used because the verse contains surprising information.
WOW (write own work): Choose the Cat worksheet, the Dog worksheet or the Rabbit worksheet, according to the ability level of each child. Support the child in following the instructions on the worksheet, to write their own work.

 Andrew Brodie: Improving Writing for ages 7–8 © A&C Black Publishers 2010

My little dog

Name

Date

Word Bank   around   just   frog   doesn't   bark   croak
completely   tries   lily   swim

Complete each verse of the poem.

My little dog

My little dog
Is a very strange dog,

The noise he makes
Is such a joke,

My little dog
Is completely mad,

When it tips
He tries to swim!

Teacher's Notes

This activity encourages children to observe the structure of a rhyming poem. It provides the opportunity for them to practise their skills in handwriting and in spelling using phonics, although many of the words they need are supplied in the word bank.

Read together: the poem on page 24, 'My little dog', then the instructions on this page and the words in the word bank. Read the first two lines of each verse that are supplied.

Talk together: Discuss the poem and illustrations with the children.

WOW (write own work): Dictate the second half of each verse, encouraging the children to write them neatly and to use appropriate spellings.

- Are most letters correctly formed and orientated? Are there appropriate spaces between words? Are upper and lower case letters distinguished? (Handwriting and presentation Level 1)
- Is there some awareness of use of full stops and capital letters? (AF6 Level 1)
- Does the child use correct spelling? (AF8 Level 1)

My little dog

Name

Date

Complete each verse of the poem.

My little dog

My little dog
Is a very strange dog,

The noise he makes
Is such a joke,

My little dog
Is completely mad,

When it tips
He tries to swim!

Teacher's Notes

This activity encourages children to observe the structure of a rhyming poem. It provides the opportunity for them to practise their skills in handwriting and in spelling using phonics.

Read together: the poem on page 24, 'My little dog', then the instructions on this page. Read the first two lines of each verse that are supplied.

Talk together: Discuss the poem and the illustrations with the children. Remind them why exclamation marks have been used.

WOW (write own work): Dictate the second half of each verse, encouraging the children to write them neatly and to use appropriate spellings.

- Are letters clearly formed, with ascenders and descenders distinguished? (Handwriting and presentation Level 2)
- Are sentences usually accurately demarcated with capital letters and full stops? Is there some accurate use of exclamation marks? (AF6 Level 2)
- Does the child use correct spelling? (AF8 Level 1)

Can you write two more verses for the poem?

My little dog

My little dog
Is a very strange dog,
He hops around,
Just like a frog!

The noise he makes
Is such a joke,
He doesn't bark,
He makes a croak!

My little dog
Is completely mad,
He tries to sit
On a lily pad!

When it tips
He tries to swim!
I have to say,
I do love him!

Teacher's Notes

This activity encourages children to observe and follow the structure of a rhyming poem.

Read together: the question and the poem on this page.

Talk together: Discuss the poem with the children.

WOW (write own work): Encourage the children to make up their own verses in a similar style to those in the poem.

- Are some appropriate ideas included? Are simple adjectives used to elaborate on information or events? Is there an attempt to adopt viewpoint? (AF1 Level 3)
- Is purpose established at a general level? Are main features of the rhyming poem form signalled to the reader? Are there some attempts to adopt the appropriate style? (AF2 Level 3)
- Is there some attempt to sequence ideas and material logically, eg with related points placed next to each other? Are openings and closings sometimes signalled? (AF3 Level 3)
- Is there some structure within sections of text? Are there some links between sentences? (AF4 Level 3)
- Is there reliance mainly on simply structured sentences, but with some variation with support? (AF5 Level 3)
- Are sentences demarcated accurately with capital letters and full stops, question marks or exclamation marks? (AF6 Level 3)
- Is appropriate vocabulary used, and are some words chosen for effect? (AF7 Level 3)
- Does the child use correct spelling? (AF8 Level 3)

On my birthday

On my birthday
I was eight.
I can tell you
The exact date.

On my birthday
I was eight.
I got a watch so
I won't be late.

On my birthday
I was eight.
Seven was good
But eight is great!

On my next birthday
I will be nine.
Eight is great but
Nine will be fine!

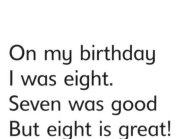

Teacher's Notes

Suggested objective: Write a poem following the style of 'On my birthday'.
Read together: the rhyming poem.
Talk together: Discuss the poem with the children, pointing out that it rhymes and that it is written in a four-line structure. Encourage the children to observe the 'traditional' style of punctuation for rhyming poetry, ie capital letters at the start of each line. Explain that the exclamation marks are used in two of the verses because they contain strong statements.
WOW (write own work): Choose the Cat worksheet, the Dog worksheet or the Rabbit worksheet, according to the ability level of each child. Support the child in following the instructions on the worksheet, to write their own work.

Andrew Brodie: Improving Writing for ages 7–8 © A&C Black Publishers 2010

On my birthday

Name

Date

Word Bank seven   exact   nine   date   watch   great

Complete each verse of the poem.

On my birthday

On my birthday
I was eight.

On my birthday
I was eight.

On my birthday
I was eight.

On my next birthday
I will be nine.

Teacher's Notes

This activity encourages children to observe the structure of a rhyming poem. It provides the opportunity for them to practise their skills in handwriting and in spelling using phonics, although many of the words they need are supplied in the word bank.

Read together: the text on page 28, 'On my birthday', then the instructions on this page and the words in the word bank. Read the first two lines of each verse that are supplied.

Talk together: Discuss the poem and illustrations with the children.

WOW (write own work): Dictate the second half of each verse, encouraging the children to write them neatly and to use appropriate spellings.

- Are most letters correctly formed and orientated? Are there appropriate spaces between words? Are upper and lower case letters distinguished? (Handwriting and presentation Level 1)
- Is there some awareness of use of full stops and capital letters? (AF6 Level 1)
- Does the child use correct spelling? (AF8 Level 1)

On my birthday

Complete each verse of the poem.

On my birthday

On my birthday
I was eight.

On my birthday
I was eight.

On my birthday
I was eight.

My next birthday
I will be nine.

Teacher's Notes

This activity encourages children to observe the structure of a rhyming poem. It provides the opportunity for them to practise their skills in handwriting and in spelling using phonics.

Read together: the text on page 28, 'On my birthday', then the instructions on this page. Read the first two lines of each verse that are supplied.

Talk together: Discuss the poem and the illustrations with the children. Remind them why exclamation marks have been used.

WOW (write own work): Dictate the second half of each verse, encouraging the children to write them neatly and to use appropriate spellings.

- Are letters clearly formed, with ascenders and descenders distinguished? (Handwriting and presentation Level 2)
- Are sentences usually accurately demarcated with capital letters and full stops? Is there some accurate use of exclamation marks? (AF6 Level 2)
- Does the child use correct spelling? (AF8 Level 1)

On my birthday

Can you write two more verses for the poem?

On my birthday

On my birthday
I was eight.
I can tell you
The exact date.

On my birthday
I was eight.
I got a watch so
I won't be late.

On my birthday
I was eight.
Seven was good
But eight is great!

On my next birthday
I will be nine.
Eight is great but
Nine will be fine!

Teacher's Notes

This activity encourages children to observe and follow the structure of a rhyming poem.

Read together: the question and the poem on this page.
Talk together: Discuss the poem with the children.
WOW (write own work): Encourage the children to make up their own verses in a similar style to those in the poem. Explain that they do not need to start with the words 'on my birthday' but could think of their own first line, to be repeated for most or all verses.

- Are some appropriate ideas included? Are simple adjectives used to elaborate on information or events? Is there an attempt to adopt viewpoint? (AF1 Level 3)
- Is purpose established at a general level? Are main features of the rhyming poem form signalled to the reader? Are there some attempts to adopt the appropriate style? (AF2 Level 3)
- Is there some attempt to sequence ideas and material logically, eg with related points placed next to each other? Are openings and closings sometimes signalled? (AF3 Level 3)
- Is there some structure within sections of text? Are there some links between sentences? (AF4 Level 3)
- Is there reliance mainly on simply structured sentences, but with some variation with support? (AF5 Level 3)
- Are sentences demarcated accurately with capital letters and full stops, question marks or exclamation marks? (AF6 Level 3)
- Is appropriate vocabulary used, and are some words chosen for effect? (AF7 Level 3)
- Does the child use correct spelling? (AF8 Level 3)

Too snowy for school

Text for Talking

Mrs Jenkins woke up early and looked out of the window. It was dark outside but she could see that the ground was covered in a blanket of white.

"Oh, dear!" she said.

She put on her dressing gown and slippers and went downstairs. She opened the back door and closed it again quickly. It was bitterly cold outside. Snow was falling and it was already quite deep on the ground.

"Oh, dear!" she said to Mr Jenkins. "Our school can't open in this weather. The cars won't be able to get through and the children will slip on the icy ground."

Later that day the school was very quiet. Nobody was there because it was closed. The playground was covered in a thick layer of snow but there were no footprints.

Some of the children stayed at home in the warm and looked out at the snow through the window. Some children went out and played on sledges. Some children built a snowman.

The next day when Mrs Jenkins woke up she found that most of the snow had melted. She was so pleased that she could open the school.

Teacher's Notes

Suggested objective: Write about a snowy day, adopting a viewpoint.

Read together: the text, consisting of a chronological story with a familiar setting.

Talk together: Discuss the story with the children.

WOW (write own work): Choose the Cat worksheet, the Dog worksheet or the Rabbit worksheet, according to the ability level of each child. Support the child in following the instructions on the worksheet, to write their own work.

Andrew Brodie: Improving Writing for ages 7–8 © A&C Black Publishers 2010

Too snowy for school

Name

Date

Word Bank   snow   school   ice   cars   open   closed
playground   thick   white   cold   warm   clothes   play
sledge   snowman   pleased   excited   cross   sad   happy

How would you feel if you looked out of the window and saw lots of snow?

What would you do first?

What would you do all day?

Teacher's Notes

Read together: the text on page 32, 'Too snowy for school', then the instructions on this page and the words in the word bank.

Talk together: Discuss the picture and the text with the children. Can they see that the text follows a chronological pattern, starting in the early morning, then giving some details of events that took place during the day, then explaining what happened the next day? Can they remember a day when it snowed? If not, can they imagine what they would do if it did snow?

WOW (write own work): Support the group in writing a sentence to answer each question.

- Are basic information and ideas conveyed through appropriate word choice and is some descriptive writing used? (AF1 Level 1)
- Is there some awareness of use of full stops and capital letters? (AF6 Level 1)
- Does the child select appropriate and effective vocabulary? (AF7 Level 1)
- Does the child use correct spelling? (AF8 Level 1)

Too snowy for school

Name

Date

How would you feel if there was lots of snow?

What would you wear on a snowy day?

What would you do?

Too snowy for school

Name

Date

Write about a snowy day.

Teacher's Notes

Read together: the text on page 32, 'Too snowy for school', then the instructions on this page.

Talk together: Discuss the picture and the text with the children. Can they see that the text follows a chronological pattern, starting in the early morning, then giving some details of events that took place during the day, then explaining what happened the next day? Can they remember a day when it snowed? If not, can they imagine what they would do if it did snow? Encourage them to notice the use of exclamation marks and the punctuation for speech.

WOW (write own work): Encourage the children to write their own short story about a snowy day, possibly including some speech.

- Are some appropriate ideas included? Are simple adjectives used to elaborate on information or events? Is there an attempt to adopt viewpoint? (AF1 Level 3)
- Is purpose established at a general level? (AF2 Level 3)
- Is there some attempt to sequence ideas and material logically, eg with related points placed next to each other? (AF3 Level 3)
- Is there some structure within sections of text? Are there some links between sentences? (AF4 Level 3)
- Are sentences demarcated accurately with capital letters and full stops, question marks or exclamation marks? Is there some use of speech punctuation? (AF6 Level 3)
- Is appropriate vocabulary used, and are some words chosen for effect? (AF7 Level 3)
- Does the child use correct spelling? (AF8 Level 3)

An exciting secret

Text for Talking

One day when we were working on our maths, the school secretary came into our classroom. She walked over to our teacher and whispered something in her ear. Our teacher looked very pleased.

"What was that about, Miss?" asked Wayne.

"I may tell you later," she said.

"Oh, please tell us, Miss," said Kerry.

"After you have finished your maths," she said.

At the end of the lesson she asked us all to be quiet.

"I have got some exciting news," she said. "We are going to have a special visitor!"

Teacher's Notes

Suggested objective: Write about something that happens in school, using correct punctuation.
Read together: the text, consisting of a story with a familiar setting.
Talk together: Discuss the tstory with the children, asking them to suggest who the special visitor could be.
WOW (write own work): Choose the Cat worksheet, the Dog worksheet or the Rabbit worksheet, according to the ability level of each child. Support the child in following the instructions on the worksheet, to write their own work.

Andrew Brodie: Improving Writing for ages 7–8 © A&C Black Publishers 2010

An exciting secret

Name

Date

Word Bank classroom teacher children child secretary
headteacher school quiet whispered whispering told said

Write about something that happened in your class.

Teacher's Notes

Read together: the text on page 36, 'An exciting secret', then the instructions on this page and the words in the word bank.

Talk together: Discuss the picture and the text with the children. Do they notice the speech marks and understand why they are used? Note that we would not expect children at Level 1 to use speech marks in their own writing. Support the group in remembering an unusual even that has taken place in the classroom. Can they describe what happened?

WOW (write own work): Help the children to write a short description of the unusual event.
- Are basic information and ideas conveyed through appropriate word choice and is some descriptive writing used? (AF1 Level 1)
- Is the text appropriate to task, reader and purpose? (AF2 Levels 1&2)
- Are events and ideas presented in appropriate order? (AF3 Level 1)
- Are there some simple connections between ideas and events? (AF4 Level 1)
- Are some sentence-like structures formed by chaining clauses together, eg by using 'and'? (AF5 Level 1)
- Is there some awareness of use of full stops and capital letters? (AF6 Level 1)
- Does the child select appropriate and effective vocabulary? (AF7 Level 1)
- Does the child use correct spelling? (AF8 Level 1)

An exciting secret

Name

Date

Write about what happens in the story.

Teacher's Notes

Read together: the text on page 36, 'An exciting secret', then the instructions on this page.

Talk together: Discuss the picture and the text with the children. Do they notice the speech marks and understand why they are used? Note that we would not expect children at Level 2 to use speech marks in their own writing. Support the group in describing the story orally. Can they think of extra details to add, such as the names of the characters and the actual message that the secretary gave to the teacher?

WOW (write own work): Support each individual in writing the story, adding more details where appropriate.

- Are there mostly relevant ideas and content and do some apt word choices create interest? Do brief comments or questions about events or actions suggest viewpoint? (AF1 Level 2)
- Is the text appropriate to task, reader and purpose? Is some basic purpose established? Are some appropriate features of the given form used? Are there some attempts to adopt the appropriate style? (AF2 Level 2)
- Is there some basic sequencing of ideas or material? Are openings and closings sometimes signalled? (AF3 Level 2)
- Are ideas grouped by content with some linking by simple pronouns? (AF4 Level 2)
- Is there some variation in sentence openings? Are there mainly simple sentences with 'and' used to connect clauses? Are the past and present tenses generally consistent? (AF5 Level 2)
- Are sentences usually accurately demarcated with capital letters and full stops and is clause structure mostly grammatically correct? (AF6 Level 2)
- Does simple vocabulary convey relevant meaning? Are there some adventurous word choices? (AF7 Level 2)
- Does the child use correct spelling? (AF8 Level 2)

An exciting secret

Name

Date

Write about what happens next in the story.

Teacher's Notes

Read together: the text on page 36, 'An exciting secret', then the instructions on this page.

Talk together: Discuss the picture and the text with the children. Do they notice the speech marks and the exclamation mark and understand why they are used? Support the group in describing the story orally. Now ask them to make some suggestions as to who the exciting visitor could be.

WOW (write own work): Encourage the children to continue the story, possibly including some speech and perhaps revealing who the exciting visitor is and why this visitor is so special.

- Are some appropriate ideas included? Are simple adjectives used to elaborate on information or events? Is there an attempt to adopt viewpoint? (AF1 Level 3)
- Is purpose established at a general level? Are main features of a selected form signalled to the reader? Are there some attempts to adopt the appropriate style? (AF2 Level 3)
- Is there some attempt to sequence ideas and material logically, eg with related points placed next to each other? Are openings and closings sometimes signalled? (AF3 Level 3)
- Is there some structure within sections of text? Are there some links between sentences? (AF4 Level 3)
- Is there reliance mainly on simply structured sentences, but with some variation with support? (AF5 Level 3)
- Are sentences demarcated accurately with capital letters and full stops, question marks or exclamation marks? Is there some use of speech punctuation? (AF6 Level 3)
- Is appropriate vocabulary used, and are some words chosen for effect? (AF7 Level 3)
- Does the child use correct spelling? (AF8 Level 3)

Paul   I like your picture.

Harry   Thank you. I like yours, too.

Paul   What is it?

Harry   Can't you tell? It's a car.

Paul   Oh, I thought it was a house.

Harry   *(Becoming cross)* No, it's a car. Anybody can see it's a car. What's your picture of?

Paul   It's a mouse.

Harry   Oh, I thought it was an elephant!

Teacher's Notes

Suggested objective: Write a short play script following the style of 'I like your picture'.

Read together: the text, consisting of a short play script.

Talk together: Discuss the script with the children, pointing out the special way that it is written. Talk about the story contained within the script: the two children are friendly at first but quickly get less friendly when Paul mistakes Harry's picture of a car for a house. Ask the children if, in their view, Harry really thought Paul's picture was of an elephant – some of the children will understand the idea of sarcasm! Ask the children to work in pairs to present the short sketch.

WOW (write own work): Choose the Cat worksheet, the Dog worksheet or the Rabbit worksheet, according to the ability level of each child. Support the child in following the instructions on the worksheet, to write their own work.

I like your picture

Continue the script.

Paul	I like your picture.
Harry	Thank you. I like yours, too.
Paul	What is it?
Harry	Can't you tell? It's a car.
Paul	Oh, I thought it was a house.
Harry	*(Becoming cross)* No, it's a car. Anybody can see it's a car. What's your picture of?
Paul	It's a mouse.
Harry	Oh, I thought it was an elephant!

Paul ....

....

Harry ....

....

Paul ....

....

Harry ....

....

Teacher's Notes

Read together: the play script on page 40, 'I like your picture', then the instructions and text on this page.
Talk together: Discuss the picture and the text with the children. Do they notice the special way that a script is presented? Support the group in devising some extra lines for the sketch.
WOW (write own work): Help the children to write a continuation of the play.
- Are basic information and ideas conveyed through appropriate word choice and is some descriptive writing used? (AF1 Level 1)
- Is the text appropriate to task, reader and purpose? (AF2 Levels 1&2)
- Are events and ideas presented in appropriate order? (AF3 Level 1)
- Are there some simple connections between ideas and events? (AF4 Level 1)
- Are some sentence-like structures formed by chaining clauses together, eg by using 'and'? (AF5 Level 1)
- Is there some awareness of use of full stops and capital letters? (AF6 Level 1)
- Does the child select appropriate and effective vocabulary? (AF7 Level 1)
- Does the child use correct spelling? (AF8 Level 1)

I like your picture

Name

Date

*What could have happened
in the sketch?*

Paul   I like your picture.

Harry   Thank you. I like yours, too.

Paul   ---

Harry   ---

Paul   ---

Harry   ---

Paul   ---

Harry   ---

Teacher's Notes

Read together: the play script on page 40, 'I like your picture', then the instructions on this page.

Talk together: Discuss the picture and the text with the children. Explain the use of the word 'sketch' and point out the layout of the script. Encourage them to come up with some ideas for what could have been said by the two children after the first two lines.

WOW (write own work): Support each individual in writing the new version of the sketch.

- Are there mostly relevant ideas and content and do some apt word choices create interest? Do brief comments or questions about events or actions suggest viewpoint? (AF1 Level 2)
- Is the text appropriate to task, reader and purpose? Is some basic purpose established? Are some appropriate features of the given form used? Are there some attempts to adopt the appropriate style? (AF2 Level 2)
- Is there some basic sequencing of ideas or material? Are openings and closings sometimes signalled? (AF3 Level 2)
- Are ideas grouped by content with some linking by simple pronouns? (AF4 Level 2)
- Is there some variation in sentence openings? Are there mainly simple sentences with 'and' used to connect clauses? Are the past and present tenses generally consistent? (AF5 Level 2)
- Are sentences usually accurately demarcated with capital letters and full stops and is clause structure mostly grammatically correct? (AF6 Level 2)
- Does simple vocabulary convey relevant meaning? Are there some adventurous word choices? (AF7 Level 2)
- Does the child use correct spelling? (AF8 Level 2)

I like your picture

Name

Date

Write your own sketch featuring Paul and Harry. You can continue on the back of the sheet if you need to.

Paul ---

Harry ---

Paul ---

Harry ---

Paul ---

Harry ---

Paul ---

Harry ---

Teacher's Notes

Read together: the play script on page 40, 'I like your picture', then the instructions on this page.

Talk together: Discuss the picture and the text with the children. Explain the use of the word 'sketch' and point out the layout of the script. Encourage them to come up with some ideas for a different sketch involving Paul and Harry.

WOW (write own work): Encourage the children to write their own short sketch, featuring the characters of Paul and Harry.

- Are some appropriate ideas included? Are simple adjectives used to elaborate on information or events? Is there an attempt to adopt viewpoint? (AF1 Level 3)
- Is purpose established at a general level? Are main features of a selected form signalled to the reader? Are there some attempts to adopt the appropriate style? (AF2 Level 3)
- Is there some attempt to sequence ideas and material logically, eg with related points placed next to each other? Are openings and closings sometimes signalled? (AF3 Level 3)
- Is there some structure within sections of text? Are there some links between sentences? (AF4 Level 3)
- Is there reliance mainly on simply structured sentences, but with some variation with support? (AF5 Level 3)
- Are sentences demarcated accurately with capital letters and full stops, question marks or exclamation marks? (AF6 Level 3)
- Is appropriate vocabulary used, and are some words chosen for effect? (AF7 Level 3)
- Does the child use correct spelling? (AF8 Level 3)

A telephone call

Telephone rings.

Sally   Hello. This is 794268.

Kate   Hello, Sally. It's Kate here.

Sally   Oh, hello Kate. How are you?

Kate   I'm fine, thanks but I'm a bit cross because the school is closed.

Sally   I didn't know that. Why is it closed?

Kate   Well, the headteacher says there's too much snow and ice.

Sally   I think she could be right. It's dangerous for the children.

Kate   I suppose that's true and the children will enjoy the extra day off school.

Sally   Shall we take them sledging instead?

Kate   Good idea!

Teacher's Notes

Suggested objective: Write a short play script following the style of 'A telephone call'.
Read together: the text, consisting of a short play script.
Talk together: Discuss the script with the children, pointing out the special way that it is written. Talk about the story contained within the script. Do the children notice that Sally manages to change Kate's view? Ask the children to work in pairs to present the short sketch.
WOW (write own work): Choose the Cat worksheet, the Dog worksheet or the Rabbit worksheet, according to the ability level of each child. Support the child in following the instructions on the worksheet, to write their own work.

   Andrew Brodie: Improving Writing for ages 7–8 © A&C Black Publishers 2010

A telephone call

Continue the script.

Telephone rings.

Sally   Hello. This is 794268.

Kate   Hello, Sally. It's Kate here.

Sally   Oh, hello Kate. How are you?

Kate   I'm fine, thanks but I'm a bit cross because the school is closed.

Sally   I didn't know that. Why is it closed?

Kate   Well, the headteacher says there's too much snow and ice.

Sally   I think she could be right. It's dangerous for the children.

Kate   I suppose that's true and the children will enjoy the extra day off school.

Sally   Shall we take them sledging instead?

Kate   Good idea!

Sally   ---

Kate   ---

Sally   ---

Kate   ---

Teacher's Notes

Read together: the script on page 44, 'A telephone call', then the instructions and text on this page.
Talk together: Discuss the picture and the text with the children. Do they notice the special way that a script is presented? Support the group in devising some extra lines for the sketch.
WOW (write own work): Help the children to write a continuation of the play.

- Are basic information and ideas conveyed through appropriate word choice and is some descriptive writing used? (AF1 Level 1)
- Is the text appropriate to task, reader and purpose? (AF2 Levels 1&2)
- Are events and ideas presented in appropriate order? (AF3 Level 1)
- Are there some simple connections between ideas and events? (AF4 Level 1)
- Are some sentence-like structures formed by chaining clauses together, eg by using 'and'? (AF5 Level 1)
- Is there some awareness of use of full stops and capital letters? (AF6 Level 1)
- Does the child select appropriate and effective vocabulary? (AF7 Level 1)
- Does the child use correct spelling? (AF8 Level 1)

A telephone call

*What could have happened
in the sketch?*

Sally   Hello. This is 794268.

Kate   Hello, Sally. It's Kate here.

Sally   ....

....

Kate   ....

....

Sally   ....

....

Kate   ....

....

Sally   ....

....

Kate   ....

....

Teacher's Notes

Read together: the script on page 44, 'A telephone call', then the instructions on this page.

Talk together: Discuss the picture and the text with the children. Explain the use of the word 'sketch' and point out the layout of the script. Encourage them to come up with some ideas for what could have been said by the two women after the first two lines.

WOW (write own work): Support each individual in writing the new version of the sketch.

- Are there mostly relevant ideas and content and do some apt word choices create interest? Do brief comments or questions about events or actions suggest viewpoint? (AF1 Level 2)
- Is the text appropriate to task, reader and purpose? Is some basic purpose established? Are some appropriate features of the given form used? Are there some attempts to adopt the appropriate style? (AF2 Level 2)
- Is there some basic sequencing of ideas or material? Are openings and closings sometimes signalled? (AF3 Level 2)
- Are ideas grouped by content with some linking by simple pronouns? (AF4 Level 2)
- Is there some variation in sentence openings? Are there mainly simple sentences with 'and' used to connect clauses? Are the past and present tenses generally consistent? (AF5 Level 2)
- Are sentences usually accurately demarcated with capital letters and full stops and is clause structure mostly grammatically correct? (AF6 Level 2)
- Does simple vocabulary convey relevant meaning? Are there some adventurous word choices? (AF7 Level 2)
- Does the child use correct spelling? (AF8 Level 2)

Andrew Brodie: Improving Writing for ages 7–8 © A&C Black Publishers 2010

A telephone call

Name

Date

Write your own sketch featuring Sally and Kate.
You can continue on the back of the sheet if you need to.

Sally --

Kate --

Sally --

Kate --

Sally --

Kate --

Sally --

Kate --

Sally --

Kate --

Teacher's Notes

Read together: the script on page 44, 'A telephone call', then the instructions on this page.
Talk together: Discuss the picture and the text with the children, encouraging them to notice the viewpoints of each character. Explain the use of the word 'sketch' and point out the layout of the script. Ask them to come up with some ideas for a different sketch involving Sally and Kate.
WOW (write own work): Encourage the children to write their own short sketch, featuring the characters of Sally and Kate.
- Are some appropriate ideas included? Are simple adjectives used to elaborate on information or events? Is there an attempt to adopt viewpoint? (AF1 Level 3)
- Is purpose established at a general level? Are main features of a selected form signalled to the reader? Are there some attempts to adopt the appropriate style? (AF2 Level 3)
- Is there some attempt to sequence ideas and material logically, eg with related points placed next to each other? Are openings and closings sometimes signalled? (AF3 Level 3)
- Is there some structure within sections of text? Are there some links between sentences? (AF4 Level 3)
- Is there reliance mainly on simply structured sentences, but with some variation with support? (AF5 Level 3)
- Are sentences demarcated accurately with capital letters and full stops, question marks or exclamation marks? (AF6 Level 3)
- Is appropriate vocabulary used, and are some words chosen for effect? (AF7 Level 3)
- Does the child use correct spelling? (AF8 Level 3)

All plants need the right conditions to grow. They need sunlight, water and food from the soil.

To grow a geranium, plant a seed in some soil in a small pot. Sprinkle some water on the soil then put the pot in a sunny place.

After about a week the seed will produce roots in the soil. Soon a pair of leaves will appear. Don't forget to water the plant regularly.

In a few weeks the plant will have grown enough to produce flowers.

Teacher's Notes

Suggested objective: Write about growing plants, using a clear structure to the text.

Read together: the text, consisting of an information piece.

Talk together: Discuss the text with the children, ensuring they understand the process of growth. Ideally they should be given the opportunity to grow some geraniums from seed

WOW (write own work): Choose the Cat worksheet, the Dog worksheet or the Rabbit worksheet, according to the ability level of each child. Support the child in following the instructions on the worksheet, to write their own work.

Growing plants

Name

Date

Word Bank | geranium regularly plant seed soil pot
roots leaves warm sunny water watering light food

All plants need --

To grow a geranium, plant a seed in some soil. It is important to remember --

----

After about a week --

In a few weeks --

Teacher's Notes

Read together: the text on page 48, 'Growing plants', then the instructions on this page and the words in the word bank
Talk together: Discuss the pictures and the text with the children. Do they notice that the text provides a set of instructions?
WOW (write own work): Help the children to complete each of the information sentences.
- Are basic information and ideas conveyed through appropriate word choice and is some descriptive writing used? (AF1 Level 1)
- Is the text appropriate to task, reader and purpose? (AF2 Levels 1&2)
- Are events and ideas presented in appropriate order? (AF3 Level 1)
- Are there some simple connections between ideas and events? (AF4 Level 1)
- Are some sentence-like structures formed by chaining clauses together, eg by using 'and'? (AF5 Level 1)
- Is there some awareness of use of full stops and capital letters? (AF6 Level 1)
- Does the child select appropriate and effective vocabulary? (AF7 Level 1)
- Does the child use correct spelling? (AF8 Level 1)

Growing plants

Name

Date

Word Bank   geranium   plant   seed   soil   pot   roots
leaves   warm   sunny   water   light   food

Write about growing plants.

_____

_____

_____

_____

_____

_____

_____

_____

Teacher's Notes

Read together: the text on page 48, 'Growing plants', then the instructions on this page and the words in the word bank.
Talk together: Discuss the pictures and the text with the children. Support the group in creating the instructions orally.
WOW (write own work): Support each individual in writing the set of instructions.

- Are there mostly relevant ideas and content and do some apt word choices create interest? (AF1 Level 2)
- Is the text appropriate to task, reader and purpose? Is some basic purpose established? Are some appropriate features of the given form used? Are there some attempts to adopt the appropriate style? (AF2 Level 2)
- Is there some basic sequencing of ideas or material? Are openings and closings sometimes signalled? (AF3 Level 2)
- Are ideas grouped by content with some linking by simple pronouns? (AF4 Level 2)
- Is there some variation in sentence openings? Are there mainly simple sentences with 'and' used to connect clauses? Are the past and present tenses generally consistent? (AF5 Level 2)
- Are sentences usually accurately demarcated with capital letters and full stops and is clause structure mostly grammatically correct? (AF6 Level 2)
- Does simple vocabulary convey relevant meaning? Are there some adventurous word choices? (AF7 Level 2)
- Does the child use correct spelling? (AF8 Level 2)

Andrew Brodie: Improving Writing for ages 7–8 © A&C Black Publishers 2010

Growing plants

Name

Date

Write about growing plants.

Teacher's Notes

Read together: the text on page 48, 'Growing plants', then the instructions on this page.

Talk together: Discuss the pictures and the text with the children. Ensure that they understand that the text contains both information and instructions.

WOW (write own work): Encourage the children to create their own text regarding growing plants.

- Are some appropriate ideas included? Are simple adjectives used to elaborate on information or events? Is there an attempt to adopt viewpoint? (AF1 Level 3)
- Is purpose established at a general level? Are main features of a selected form signalled to the reader? Are there some attempts to adopt the appropriate style? (AF2 Level 3)
- Is there some attempt to sequence ideas and material logically, eg with related points placed next to each other? Are openings and closings sometimes signalled? (AF3 Level 3)
- Is there some structure within sections of text? Are there some links between sentences? (AF4 Level 3)
- Is there reliance mainly on simply structured sentences, but with some variation with support? (AF5 Level 3)
- Are sentences demarcated accurately with capital letters and full stops? AF6 Level 3)
- Is appropriate vocabulary used, and are some words chosen for effect? (AF7 Level 3)
- Does the child use correct spelling? (AF8 Level 3)

A walk in the woods

Yesterday our class went for a walk in the woods. We had to wear our Wellington boots because the teacher said the woods would be muddy. She was right!

When we were in the woods we had to stand still and be really quiet. When we were quiet we could hear lots of sounds. We could hear the leaves moving in the wind. We could hear birds singing in the trees. We could hear an aeroplane and we could hear traffic on the motorway.

We saw lots of things as well. We saw flowers growing on the ground. We saw birds flying through the trees. We saw bright green leaves on the trees.

When we got back to school we had to take off our muddy boots.

Teacher's Notes

Suggested objective: Write about a walk, using a clear structure to the text.
Read together: the text, consisting of a report story.
Talk together: Discuss the tatory with the children, encouraging them to think about a walk or trip they have had as a class.
Ideally the class could take a walk in woods, in the streets or even in the school grounds, stopping regularly to look and listen.
WOW (write own work): Choose the Cat worksheet, the Dog worksheet or the Rabbit worksheet, according to the ability level of each child. Support the child in following the instructions on the worksheet, to write their own work.

A walk in the woods

Name

Date

walk   woods   grounds   beach   street
town   city   village   countryside   seaside   school

*Can you write about
a walk you went on?*

Where we went

What we saw

What we heard

Teacher's Notes

Read together: the text on page 52, 'A walk in the woods', then the instructions on this page and the words in the word bank.
Talk together: Discuss the text with the children then look at the sub-heading. Encourage each of them to compose an oral sentence for each sub-heading.
WOW (write own work): Support the pupils in writing a report based on the oral report they have already given.
- Are basic information and ideas conveyed through appropriate word choice and is some descriptive writing used? (AF1 Level 1)
- Is the text appropriate to task, reader and purpose? (AF2 Levels 1&2)
- Are events and ideas presented in appropriate order? (AF3 Level 1)
- Are there some simple connections between ideas and events? (AF4 Level 1)
- Are some sentence-like structures formed by chaining clauses together, eg by using 'and'? (AF5 Level 1)
- Is there some awareness of use of full stops and capital letters? (AF6 Level 1)
- Does the child select appropriate and effective vocabulary? (AF7 Level 1)
- Does the child use correct spelling? (AF8 Level 1)

A walk in the woods

Name

Date

Can you write about
a walk you went on?
Where did you go?
What did you see?
What did you hear?
What did you do when
you got back?

A walk

Teacher's Notes

Read together: the text on page 52, 'A walk in the woods', then the instructions on this page including the prompts.

Talk together: Discuss the text with the children then talk about the prompts, pointing out the structure that they create. They may notice that the prompts ask for information in a different order to that presented on page 52. Help the children to compose orally a sentence related to each prompt.

WOW (write own work): Support the children in writing at least one sentence for each section of the report.

- Are there mostly relevant ideas and content and do some apt word choices create interest? Do brief comments or questions about events or actions suggest viewpoint? (AF1 Level 2)
- Is the text appropriate to task, reader and purpose? Is some basic purpose established? Are some appropriate features of the given form used? Are there some attempts to adopt the appropriate style? (AF2 Level 2)
- Is there some basic sequencing of ideas or material? (AF3 Level 2)
- Are sentences usually accurately demarcated with capital letters and full stops and is clause structure mostly grammatically correct? (AF6 Level 2)
- Does simple vocabulary convey relevant meaning? Are there some adventurous word choices? (AF7 Level 2)
- Does the child use correct spelling? (AF8 Level 2)

A walk in the woods

Name

Date

Write about a walk.

A walk

Teacher's Notes

Read together: the text on page 52, 'A walk in the woods', then the instructions on this page.
Talk together: Discuss the text with the children. Can they observe the structure of the report?
WOW (write own work): Encourage the children to write about a walk they have experienced using a similar structure for their writing as that on page 52.

- Are some appropriate ideas included? Are simple adjectives used to elaborate on information or events? Is there an attempt to adopt viewpoint? (AF1 Level 3)
- Is purpose established at a general level? (AF2 Level 3)
- Is there some attempt to sequence ideas and material logically, eg with related points placed next to each other? (AF3 Level 3)
- Is there some structure within sections of text? Are there some links between sentences? (AF4 Level 3)
- Are sentences demarcated accurately with capital letters and full stops, question marks or exclamation marks? (AF6 Level 3)
- Is appropriate vocabulary used, and are some words chosen for effect? (AF7 Level 3)
- Does the child use correct spelling? (AF8 Level 3)

The old house

Max and Zena looked into the house through a dusty window. They could tell that nobody was living there. The window was covered in cobwebs. There were no curtains and there was no furniture.

"Do you think it's safe to go in?" asked Max.

"It might not be. I don't think we should go in," said Zena.

"Oh come on, let's see if the door will open," said Max.

"All right," said Zena, but she was very scared.

The two children pushed their way through the tall grass to the front door. Max reached up for the handle and gave the door a push. It creaked open slowly.

"Who's there?" came a loud voice from inside the house.

Andrew Brodie: Improving Writing for ages 7–8 © A&C Black Publishers 2010

The old house

Name

Date

Word Bank   house   cobwebs   furniture   curtains
upstairs   downstairs   window   garden

Write about visiting an old house.

Teacher's Notes

Read together: the text on page 56, 'The old house', then the instructions on this page and the words in the word bank.

Talk together: Discuss the picture and the text with the children. If children have never been to an old house, ask them to write about any house. Do they notice the speech marks and understand why they are used? Note that we would not expect children at Level 1 to use speech marks in their own writing. Support the group in creating orally a story about an old house. If you wish you could ask the children simply to repeat what happened in the story on page 56.

WOW (write own work): Help the children to write a short story about visiting an old house – they may choose to repeat the story from page 56 but using their own words.

- Are basic information and ideas conveyed through appropriate word choice and is some descriptive writing used? (AF1 Level 1)
- Is the text appropriate to task, reader and purpose? (AF2 Levels 1&2)
- Are events and ideas presented in appropriate order? (AF3 Level 1)
- Are there some simple connections between ideas and events? (AF4 Level 1)
- Are some sentence-like structures formed by chaining clauses together, eg by using 'and'? (AF5 Level 1)
- Is there some awareness of use of full stops and capital letters? (AF6 Level 1)
- Does the child select appropriate and effective vocabulary? (AF7 Level 1)
- Does the child use correct spelling? (AF8 Level 1)

The old house

Name

Date

Write about what happens in the story.

Teacher's Notes

Read together: the text on page 56, 'The old house', then the instructions on this page.

Talk together: Discuss the picture and the text with the children. Do they notice the speech marks and understand why they are used? Note that we would not expect children at Level 2 to use speech marks in their own writing. Support the group in describing the story orally. Can they think of extra details to add, such as what could have happened next?

WOW (write own work): Support each individual in rewriting the story, adding more details where appropriate and extending it to show what could have happened next.

- Are there mostly relevant ideas and content and do some apt word choices create interest? Do brief comments or questions about events or actions suggest viewpoint? (AF1 Level 2)
- Is the text appropriate to task, reader and purpose? Is some basic purpose established? Are some appropriate features of the given form used? Are there some attempts to adopt the appropriate style? (AF2 Level 2)
- Is there some basic sequencing of ideas or material? Are openings and closings sometimes signalled? (AF3 Level 2)
- Are ideas grouped by content with some linking by simple pronouns? (AF4 Level 2)
- Is there some variation in sentence openings? Are there mainly simple sentences with 'and' used to connect clauses? Are the past and present tenses generally consistent? (AF5 Level 2)
- Are sentences usually accurately demarcated with capital letters and full stops and is clause structure mostly grammatically correct? (AF6 Level 2)
- Does simple vocabulary convey relevant meaning? Are there some adventurous word choices? (AF7 Level 2)
- Does the child use correct spelling? (AF8 Level 2)

The old house

Name

Date

Write about what happens next in the story.

Teacher's Notes

Read together: the text on page 56, 'The old house', then the instructions on this page.

Talk together: Discuss the picture and the text with the children. Do they notice the speech marks and the exclamation mark and understand why they are used? Support the group in describing the story orally. Now ask them to make some suggestions as to what could happen next.

WOW (write own work): Encourage the children to continue the story, possibly including some speech.

- Are some appropriate ideas included? Are simple adjectives used to elaborate on information or events? Is there an attempt to adopt viewpoint? (AF1 Level 3)
- Is purpose established at a general level? Are main features of a selected form signalled to the reader? Are there some attempts to adopt the appropriate style? (AF2 Level 3)
- Is there some attempt to sequence ideas and material logically, eg with related points placed next to each other? Are openings and closings sometimes signalled? (AF3 Level 3)
- Is there some structure within sections of text? Are there some links between sentences? (AF4 Level 3)
- Is there reliance mainly on simply structured sentences, but with some variation with support? (AF5 Level 3)
- Are sentences demarcated accurately with capital letters and full stops, question marks or exclamation marks? Is there some use of speech punctuation? (AF6 Level 3)
- Is appropriate vocabulary used, and are some words chosen for effect? (AF7 Level 3)
- Does the child use correct spelling? (AF8 Level 3)

Climbing the tree

Danny reached up with his hands to grab a branch then stepped up on to another branch with his foot. He kept climbing up the tree until he reached a part where the branches were too thin. He stopped climbing and looked around.

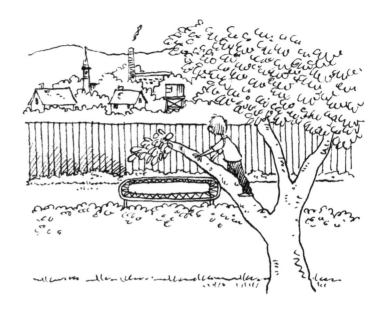

He could see over the fence into the garden next door. They had a trampoline. He wished he had a trampoline.

Looking the other way, Danny could see for miles. He could see the roofs of houses, an old water tower, a church spire and the chimney of a factory. In the distance there were green hills. Danny was happy. He loved staring at the view.

Suddenly the tree began to shake. Was it the wind blowing it? No!

Danny looked down. He couldn't see much because there were so many leaves.

The tree was shaking more and more. Danny realised that somebody else was climbing the tree!

Teacher's Notes

Suggested objective: Write imaginatively, following the style of 'Climbing the tree'.
Read together: the text, consisting of a story with a mystery or adventure theme.
Talk together: Discuss the story with the children, asking them to suggest what could happen next.
WOW (write own work): Choose the Cat worksheet, the Dog worksheet or the Rabbit worksheet, according to the ability level of each child. Support the child in following the instructions on the worksheet, to write their own work.

 Andrew Brodie: Improving Writing for ages 7–8 © A&C Black Publishers 2010

Climbing the tree

Name

Date

| Word Bank | tree view garden fence factory houses roofs chimney church tower somebody something scared frightened |

Write about climbing a tree.

Climbing the tree

Name

Date

Write about what happens in the story.

Teacher's Notes

Read together: the text on page 60, 'Climbing the tree', then the instructions on this page.

Talk together: Discuss the picture and the text with the children. Support the group in describing the story orally. Can they think of extra details to add, such as what could have happened next?

WOW (write own work): Support each individual in rewriting the story, adding more details where appropriate and extending it to show what could have happened next.

- Are there mostly relevant ideas and content and do some apt word choices create interest? Do brief comments or questions about events or actions suggest viewpoint? (AF1 Level 2)
- Is the text appropriate to task, reader and purpose? Is some basic purpose established? Are some appropriate features of the given form used? Are there some attempts to adopt the appropriate style? (AF2 Level 2)
- Is there some basic sequencing of ideas or material? Are openings and closings sometimes signalled? (AF3 Level 2)
- Are ideas grouped by content with some linking by simple pronouns? (AF4 Level 2)
- Is there some variation in sentence openings? Are there mainly simple sentences with 'and' used to connect clauses? Are the past and present tenses generally consistent? (AF5 Level 2)
- Are sentences usually accurately demarcated with capital letters and full stops and is clause structure mostly grammatically correct? (AF6 Level 2)
- Does simple vocabulary convey relevant meaning? Are there some adventurous word choices? (AF7 Level 2)
- Does the child use correct spelling? (AF8 Level 2)

 Andrew Brodie: Improving Writing for ages 7–8 © A&C Black Publishers 2010

Climbing the tree

Name

Date

Write about what happens next in the story.

Teacher's Notes

Read together: the text on page 60, 'Climbing the tree', then the instructions on this page.

Talk together: Discuss the picture and the text with the children. Support the group in describing the story orally. Now ask them to make some suggestions as to what could happen next.

WOW (write own work): Encourage the children to continue the story.

- Are some appropriate ideas included? Are simple adjectives used to elaborate on information or events? Is there an attempt to adopt viewpoint? (AF1 Level 3)
- Is purpose established at a general level? Are main features of a selected form signalled to the reader? Are there some attempts to adopt the appropriate style? (AF2 Level 3)
- Is there some attempt to sequence ideas and material logically, eg with related points placed next to each other? Are openings and closings sometimes signalled? (AF3 Level 3)
- Is there some structure within sections of text? Are there some links between sentences? (AF4 Level 3)
- Is there reliance mainly on simply structured sentences, but with some variation with support? (AF5 Level 3)
- Are sentences demarcated accurately with capital letters and full stops, question marks or exclamation marks? Is there some use of speech punctuation? (AF6 Level 3)
- Is appropriate vocabulary used, and are some words chosen for effect? (AF7 Level 3)
- Does the child use correct spelling? (AF8 Level 3)

Class record sheet

You may find it helpful to record which sheets each child has completed. You could use a green pen to record 'Rabbit' worksheets, an orange pen to record 'Dog' worksheets and a red pen to record 'Cat' worksheets.

Name	My summer holidays – recount	A drink for a crow – fable	The fox and the crow – fable	Autumn leaves – poem	My little dog – poem	On my birthday – poem	Too snowy for school – story	An exciting secret – mystery	I like your picture – dialogue	A telephone call – dialogue	Growing plants – instructional text	A walk in the woods – recount	The old house – mystery	Climbing the tree – adventure

Andrew Brodie: Improving Writing for ages 7–8 © A&C Black Publishers 2010